Lucas's Story

Our Family's Journey Through Youth Concussion Recovery

Melissa Malone-Soutuyo

Lucas's Story: Our Family's Journey Through Youth Concussion Recovery

Printed in the United States of America.

First printing 2019

ISBN: 978-0-578-62094-7

DEDICATION

To Moriah: Thank you from the bottom of my heart for reaching out to me when you learned what we were going through. Without you, I shudder to think of how much longer it would have taken us to find our way. Thank you for your friendship and for continuing to check in on Lucas from time to time. You will now and forever be considered one of our family's guardian angels.

To John: Thank you for being a friend to my family and myself for so many years. You are my first call, on speed dial, when it comes to these things. Thank you for your patience, your expertise, always being there for me, being able to put me at ease, and doing it with the same wicked sense of humor that I enjoy. I am grateful for you.

To Mike: Thank you just isn't a big enough word. You have helped my family in more ways than you even know. From educating us to putting us at ease, you helped bring the confidence and swagger back to our family. We trust you implicitly. Thank you for being a friend to me, but also for being a friend and confidante for Lucas. His visits to you were the bright spot in his days, during the days when he was really struggling. I am so grateful for your presence in his life and in ours. You are a gift to us. Thank you.

To Angel: Thank you for being my partner in life and in parenting. It's certainly no easy ride raising children, and yet, here we are killing it! But, seriously, who knew that this would be the glue that our family needed? If there's any silver lining in any of this, it is that. Our communication skills, empathy and teamwork were all forced to improve for the sake of our son, and ultimately, it also strengthened our relationship with each other. Thank you for your commitment to me and to our family. I couldn't do this without you. I love you.

To Mom and Dad: Dad, thank you for giving me the courage and permission to dream of doing great things. Mom, thank you for teaching me the discipline and work ethic to achieve my dreams. I could never accomplish half of the things I've done in my life or be half the parent that I'm always striving to be, without your examples. Thank you for giving me what I have inside. I love and miss you both.

To Lucas: Thank you for choosing me to be your mom. I love that you "always knew it would work". Thank you for your courage in letting me tell your story. Thank you for trying so hard at everything you do. You never settle and I will never settle when it comes to being your #1 fan, teammate and advocate. I love you beyond measure.

TABLE OF CONTENTS

CHAPTER 7

PREFACE

Thank you for reading our story. It is meant to serve as a guide for parents that want to learn more about youth concussion. It is also a story about my son, Lucas, and his journey through multiple concussions, post-concussion syndrome, treatment and recovery.

As a disclaimer, this book is not meant to serve as a medical guide. I am not a physician or a medical provider, specializing in concussion. This is simply our family's experience, including things we've learned along the way. Each person's experience will be different. This book should in no way replace or override the expertise of your medical professional or concussion treatment team.

Our family feels strongly that concussions must be taken very seriously and treated appropriately. This book stemmed from the passion we have to make sure this type of injury is taken seriously, and is hopefully the start of a conversation among families with young athletes, our children's coaches and our communities. The more we can raise awareness about the seriousness and severity of head injuries in our children, the better we can manage them. This will only help us to recognize them more, deal with them properly and hopefully even prevent them as much as possible. Our children's brains and futures depend on us.

CHAPTER 1

Lucas's Story

He was in 6th grade. My son, Lucas, had been skating and playing hockey almost from the time he could walk. Playing hockey became his dream from the time he was a toddler, and by the time he was in 1st grade, he had a Division I college picked out, with a goal of playing on their hockey team. It's a lofty goal, but my point is, he loved and still loves hockey so much that it has always been a source of passion and excitement for our whole family.

So, you can imagine our excitement the day Lucas got a call from his middle school coach, asking him to play a game with the varsity team. As a 6th grader, and his first year playing middle school hockey, he had settled into a role as a leader on the junior varsity team, scoring goals in every game he had played. Getting the call up to play with the 7th and 8th graders on the varsity team felt like such a huge accomplishment and he was both nervous and excited.

That night my husband and I sat in the stands, watching the game and remarking how little Lucas looked out there and how well he was holding his own. I was even snapping pictures on my phone of him being paired up, on a line, against a kid twice his size. We were really enjoying ourselves and our team was winning! The game was almost over and the other team was beginning to get frustrated. The next thing I knew, Lucas went into a corner to play the puck and a kid from the other team pushed him from behind, head first into the boards. It was one of those terrifying moments in hockey where a player goes down and the arena goes silent. It was, hands down, the number one most terrifying moment I've experienced as a parent, and I've had to give my child the Heimlich maneuver for choking… twice. The only noise throughout the arena was my child's blood curdling screams.

My husband was an athletic trainer in professional hockey for nearly 15 years, so he ran to the ice to assess our son, leaving me in the stands alone, while I felt the uncomfortable glances of all the other parents, looking over at me. As a trained occupational therapist, I started quickly scanning my brain through every scary diagnosis I could think of. Spinal cord injury and brain bleeds were topping the list and I sat with bated breath as he was assessed on the ice by my husband, the athletic trainer, and a sports medicine physician, who was also in attendance. It seemed like an eternity that he lay there as my mind went wild. My fears were tempered, for only a few moments, as they helped him to his feet, and all but carried him off the ice. I was feeling confident as there was no spine board and no ambulance called.

I rushed to the lobby and waited for my husband and son to emerge from the locker room. As they approached me, Lucas was walking on his own, but my husband was shaking his head, mouthing the words, "It's not good."

Panic overtook my entire body once again, as we loaded my son into the car and headed for the hospital. His hands and feet were still numb and he was still crying way too hard to ease any of my anxiety.

Once at the hospital, we answered all the triage questions, Lucas was put into a neck brace and we were put into a room immediately. When they came to take him away to have a CT scan and MRI, my husband and I both broke down into quiet sobs as they wheeled him away.

When he returned, he was in good spirits, the crying had stopped, his numbness was gone and I was thanking God, thinking the worst was behind us. We waited, almost gleefully, for the normal radiology reports to be returned. Sure enough, no spinal damage or brain bleeds and we were free to go! Little did we know, we were still about to embark on the greatest challenge of any of our lives.

CHAPTER 2

Concussion

What is <u>concussion?</u>

According to the American Association of Neurological Surgeons, a concussion is "an injury to the brain that results in temporary loss of normal brain function" and the formal medical definition is a clinical syndrome characterized by immediate and transient alteration in brain function, including alteration of mental status and level of consciousness, resulting from mechanical force or trauma." (1)

What are the signs and symptoms of a concussion?

Symptoms can be physical, mental and emotional. They may occur immediately after the injury or it may take days or weeks for signs and symptoms to appear. Some last for seconds and others may linger. It is important to recognize signs and symptoms so that the child can receive proper treatment. Any and all of the following could be signs of a concussion:

- Confusion or feeling dazed
- Clumsiness
- Slurred speech
- Nausea and/or vomiting
- Headache
- Ringing in ears
- Concentration difficulties
- Balance problems or dizziness
- Blurred vision
- Sensitivity to light
- Sensitivity to noise
- Sluggishness
- Behavior or personality changes
- Memory loss

These are not all of the signs and symptom possibilities and each injury can create a completely different set of symptoms. (2)

Upon returning home from the hospital, Lucas had none of the above symptoms, with the exception of sheer exhaustion from experiencing such a traumatic event and evening. As a precaution, I kept him home from school for the next two days. When I was confident he was in the clear, he returned to school and was back to playing hockey within a week. We were relieved and grateful for his good fortune and speedy recovery to perfect health.

Fast forward about a month. In another hockey game, he sustained another blow to the right side of his head, after being knocked into the boards. This time we did not fear an injury to his neck, but we knew he was already exhibiting signs and symptoms of a concussion. We did not go to the hospital and took him home to rest. He was out of school for a week with headaches and fatigue.

This time around, Lucas's headaches were intense and lingering. After a week at home from school, with no television, electronics or running around (try getting an 11 year-old to abstain from all of those activities!), he couldn't even ride in a car without getting a headache and I was concerned, to say the least. We sent him back to school because we didn't know what else to do, and he was falling behind in his studies rapidly. We now know that was a mistake.

After about a month with symptoms, I made an appointment for him to see a neurologist. I wanted the neurologist to explain to Lucas why he was not able to return to hockey at that time. My son was determined to return to his team in time for playoffs and we knew that he couldn't. He wasn't taking that news well from us so I wanted the neurologist to be the one to tell him that his season was over and why. He did, of course, and explained the seriousness of protecting his head and preventing secondary impact syndrome. He also assured him that most concussions heal within the first 60 days and he would likely soon be feeling just fine.

After almost 3 months, I posted something on social media, mentioning my son's lingering concussion symptoms. It was at that time when everything started to turn around. An old occupational therapy classmate and friend of mine,

Moriah, reached out to me. Unbeknownst to me, she was specialized in and practicing as a concussion specialist O.T. I had left the field of O.T. 12 years prior and had no idea there was such a thing. My husband is also a retired athletic trainer, who worked in professional hockey for nearly 15 years, and neither of us knew there had been so much progress in the field of concussion. It used to be that the only treatment was to rest your brain by avoiding activities that increased your symptoms and slowly return to activities as tolerated.

Moriah was working in a hospital 2 hours from our home, but we made Lucas an appointment and waited anxiously to see her.

CHAPTER 3

Concussion Rehab

- Is there treatment for concussions?

- Who should my child see for a concussion as part of the treatment team?

- What is post-concussion syndrome?

The amazing news is yes! Yes, there is actually treatment for concussions and post-concussion syndrome. Post-concussion syndrome is a set of symptoms that may continue for weeks, months or a year or more after a concussion – a mild form of traumatic brain injury.

If your child sustains a concussion, the first thing you must do is rule out anything more serious and determine if a trip to the emergency room is necessary. Not every concussion requires a trip to the ER, however, if any of the following symptoms are present, then a trip to the ER should be on your list: (3)

- Confusion or disorientation
- A headache accompanied by nausea and/ or vomiting
- Evidence of deteriorating mental status

Also, if your child experiences any of the following symptoms within 24 hours of a head injury, EVEN if he/she felt okay at the time of injury, then you need to go to the emergency room: (3)

- Unusual behavior or confusion
- Progressive or worsening symptoms
- Weakness, numbness, slurred speech
- Difficulty with eye movements
- Worsening or severe headache
- Seizure
- Vomiting multiple times
- Difficulty waking or arousing
- Discharge of clear fluid or blood from the nose or ears

Once these things have been ruled out, then healing can begin. Knowing what we know now, I would have immediately scheduled Lucas to see a concussion specialist. A concussion specialist could be a neurologist, a neuropsychologist or a number of other medical professionals who have dedicated themselves to specializing in concussion. Based on the results of that evaluation, recommendations may include follow-up appointments with other specialists, including but not limited to a radiologist for MRI, a headache specialist, a vision specialist such as a neurobehavioral optometrist, balance/vestibular specialists such as occupational therapists and physical therapists, as well as others.

Lucas was finally evaluated by my friend and classmate, Moriah, at a hospital two hours from our home. She was able to identify both musculoskeletal issues in his neck as well as an oculomotor spasm (eye spasm) immediately and sent us home with recommendations for a neurobehavioral optometrist and a physical therapist close to our home. After reaching out to some other acquaintances in the concussion community, I also discovered a chiropractic neurologist in our area that specialized in concussion. I should note that at this time, Lucas had had symptoms for more than 90 days and was diagnosed with post-concussion syndrome.

Once he began therapy with both the chiropractic neurologist and physical therapist, we began seeing improvements in his symptoms immediately and we were all beginning to feel relieved and hopeful.

It was still a heck of a long haul until he was considered healed, however. He began rehab at the beginning of April. He would leave school early 3 days a week to go to some type of therapy appointment. He also had exercises for his eyes and exercises for his neck that he was responsible for doing at home daily, outside of his appointments. It was grueling at first. My husband and I would have to nag him to complete his exercises. Sometimes the exercises would make his symptoms worse and he would have to quit, and he would get so frustrated.

Lucas was in therapy until the second week of August. He was cleared and discharged from therapy just before our family's summer vacation and his goal was to be cleared by then so that he could go on waterslides while on vacation! He was! It seemed like such a small goal and something most of our kids take for granted, but for Lucas, it felt like he was on top of the world when he finally got to that point.

CHAPTER 4

The Emotional Impact of Concussion

Having your activity limited or your routines disrupted is a complete inconvenience for any of us. We've all sprained an ankle or a wrist and been frustrated by not being able to write or walk or carry groceries. The longer these injuries linger, the more the frustration level rises and that's when people can begin to experience anxiety and depression. The same is true when somebody sustains a concussion. Yes, the person is likely able to walk or write, but imagine being told to rest your brain…and your eyes. Where does one even begin with that? Imagine getting a headache every time you tried to read the instructions on a box of macaroni and cheese. Imagine being told you have to refrain from all reading for an undetermined period of time, and hence having to have someone read absolutely EVERYTHING to you. Imagine going to work or school and being told to pay attention and listen, but not look at the blackboard or computer. You can begin to imagine how frustrating and all-encompassing that could be. And just as with physical injuries and limitations, the longer the injury lingers, the more the frustration levels rise and eventually feelings of depression and hopelessness can creep in.

Lucas was no exception to this aspect of concussion recovery. At 11 years-old, he had a full life and schedule that included school, sports teams and social activities with family and friends. Due to his oculomotor spasm, he was restricted from all reading and other visual activities, including television and video games. Being a sports fanatic, especially for hockey, he wanted to enjoy watching hockey playoffs on television. However, since he wasn't allowed to look at the screen, he would sit back to, away from the television, and listen to the game. Since he wasn't allowed to jump around or participate in activities that increased his blood pressure, which would cause blood to rush to his head and exacerbate his symptoms, it made it very difficult for him to manifest his excitement when his favorite team would score or win a game. So, sitting still, back to, and keeping his celebrations to a minimum was the best he could do. His physical activity was restricted to a minimum based on his tolerance and keeping his symptoms and head pain at bay, so he was limited to slowly shooting baskets in our driveway for months. That became his favorite activity. Did I mention no video games? Yeah, that was painful and all I have to say about that.

At school, most of his teachers were very understanding. Even if they weren't, he was sent to school with a set of medical restrictions that had to be legally adhered to. He was not allowed to read. Period. He was also not allowed to write because he wasn't able to focus his eyes on the paper. This meant sitting with his back to the blackboard at times, as well as having to go sit in the office if there were activities going on in the classroom where it would be difficult to adhere to his restrictions. Some of his teachers, for instance, his literature teacher, assigned him a buddy. That meant he would sit out in the hallway with his buddy, while his buddy would read to him from whatever book they were working on in class.

At recess, Lucas would either sit on the steps, watching his friends play football or basketball. Sometimes, he would try to referee, being careful not to get into the mix. Other days, he would feel so frustrated by not being able to participate, that he would stay inside for recess altogether.

After school, he would come home and be at the mercy of his father or myself in order to complete his homework. This meant that my husband and I essentially became 6th grade students. After a full day of work, we would come home and split duty between preparing dinner and doing homework. Science, history and literature were all consuming. We would read all of the chapters and lessons from the book, while Lucas would do his best to pay attention and absorb the material by listening. Let me assure you that when you are 11, listening to your mother read to you about the properties of covalent bonds, is not the easiest information to sit and retain and answer questions about. Math was essentially impossible because it required him to look down at the paper, which he could not tolerate. Most days, math had to be put off. As hard as he tried to keep up with the work, it was impossible and he was always feeling like he was falling behind. As a student in a small, private school, his work load was rigorous and plentiful. I should note that all of his work had to be made up at a later time, as he began to get better, which doubled his already heavy work load and his stress level.

On the weekends, Lucas still wanted to go to his hockey games. He would sit in the locker room with his teammates before the game and cheer them on while they were on the ice. Though he enjoyed being there with his teammates, he felt left out and as though he was no longer really a part of the team. It definitely made him feel frustrated and sad.

Friends from school would invite him to social outings, birthday parties and sleepovers, but most of the time, he wasn't able to go. For instance, one birthday party consisted of a pizza party, a trip to the movies, followed by a sleepover. Lucas attended the pizza party portion of the party and then we picked him up. He couldn't go to the movies because he couldn't look at the screen and he couldn't sleep over because, well...you know what sleepovers are like. Sleep doesn't usually happen much and Lucas needed to keep a close eye on his sleep hygiene, ensuring plenty of time to rest his brain on a regular schedule, or else his headache symptoms would rear their ugly head and set him back. His friend circle was limited to the friends who were willing to help him adhere to his restrictions and that was difficult. But, thank God, there were a few who stayed right by his side and were especially supportive during his recovery. Needless to say, at times it felt pretty socially isolating.

This went on for months. It was exhausting...for everybody in our family, but especially for Lucas. There were nights I would tuck him into bed and his eyes would well up with tears and he would say, "Mom, I don't think I'm ever going to get better."

I would assure him he would, and he would turn over and cry himself to sleep. It was excruciating as a parent to watch my lively, energetic boy, become so limited and sad, even though I was confident he would get better.

When you break and arm, you know you're going to be in a cast for a number of weeks and then you're going to come out completely healed. When you have a head injury, there are so many variables that come into play, including setbacks, that you have no idea when you are going to be healed, or what thing or activity might be the wrong thing, and cause a setback, and there's really no objective way to predict it or measure it.

CHAPTER 5

*Behavioral Changes
and Challenges*

As the months went by, I started becoming concerned about other areas of Lucas's development. I mean, I was watching him like a hawk day and night and I was extremely sensitive to any changes in his moods or personality. It seemed to me he was losing his temper and blowing up over the smallest things and situations. I kept telling myself that it was to be expected because of the frustration he was enduring on a daily basis and the depression he was likely feeling.

But, if I was really honest with myself in my quiet moments, I knew there was something else going on. Tears were an everyday occurrence at that point in our house and we were all on edge. Lucas has always been sensitive, so becoming emotional with frustration didn't bother me so much. It was the angry under-current that always seemed to be present, and that was definitely new. It's hard to explain, but as parents, we know our kids well, and we know when something is "off" and something was most definitely off. I felt it when he spoke, and I observed it in his interactions with me, with his friends and even with our new puppy. It was different enough that it made me feel uncomfortable, as if I was living with a child that I hardly knew, and one that seemed to be changing before my eyes.

It was easy to make excuses for his moods, and it was difficult to know whether he was experiencing normal, developmental, hormonal mood swings, or something else. I would talk to parents of other boys his age and they all claimed mood swings were occurring in their homes as well. Still, as time went on, I couldn't shake the feeling that something wasn't right and I set out to find Lucas an anger manage-ment counselor, just in case.

Lucas fought us tooth and nail on seeing the counselor, and once he began therapy, he still wasn't liking it any better. I kept encouraging him to stick it out and telling him it was great to learn about healthy coping skills and life balance, regardless of whether he believed he needed to be there or not.

Week after week he complained about going. I was frustrated and I was scared. I was worried that my sweet little boy that I'd known for eleven years was gone. My husband and I got to sit in on a session and the let the counselor know of our concerns and observations. It was difficult to even articulate what was happening at home because it mostly seemed to be intangible, with a definite anger component. But, it was unpredictable. It didn't have a pattern and the occurrences appeared to happen at random times. The counselor worked with Lucas throughout the summer, asking about his week and teaching him coping skills.

Finally, in August, the counselor told me he really didn't think Lucas needed to be in therapy and that he seemed to be behaving "normally" for a boy his age. I actually had to agree. Somewhere along the way, things had really settled down at home. Lucas seemed to be acting more like himself, and without realizing it, my worry over that part of his life was slowly dissipating. This happened to be around the same time that he graduated from physical therapy. His head injury was healed, his headaches were gone, and like a light switch, his personality was back to his normal. My sweet, little boy was back.

At that point, I was starting to put the pieces together. I started thinking that maybe the behavioral changes Lucas had been exhibiting were actually a part of his injury. When I mentioned it to his counselor, he agreed. I had neglected to tell him about Lucas's head injury at the start. It hadn't seemed important or relevant at the time.

According to the Family Caregiver Alliance, head injury survivors may experience a range of neuropsychological problems following the injury, and varying based on location and severity of the injury. Among those problems can be, but are not limited to: personality changes, memory and judgment deficits, lack of impulse control and poor concentration. (4)

CHAPTER 6

Conclusion

These days Lucas is doing great. By all medical standards, he has completely healed. He actually sustained another concussion since the ones written about here, from basketball of all things. Thankfully, having the knowledge and experience we have now, we were able to quickly get him into therapy, and his recovery was much speedier.

Our lives have changed forever, however. I am much more vigilant and worried whenever Lucas does anything. Things that I wouldn't bat an eye at in the past now cause me stress and anxiety. Pool parties where kids start pushing each other off rafts, wrestling matches on the lawn, pillow fights in the living room, all cause me to jump to attention much sooner than they would have in a previous lifetime. The joy of watching my son play hockey, and any sport really, has sadly been dampened significantly.

It is not possible to keep our children in a bubble and protected from everything there is out there that can hurt them, and that feels more apparent to me every time he steps on a field, rides a bike or climbs a tree. It sounds silly, but it's changed the way I experience parenting and experience my son's life. My husband and I have had a number of people ask us how we can still allow Lucas to play hockey. But, the truth is, there is no "safe" sport or activity, and you've got to find balance in letting your child participate in activities that he/she loves, while also trying to make the best decisions to keep him/her safe. Lucas got a concussion playing basketball, kids collide on playgrounds at recess, toddlers fall off slides in day care. People bump their heads all the time. The best thing we can do is be educated so that we can recognize these injuries for what they are, take them seriously and treat them appropriately.

I thank God that Lucas doesn't appear to have any residual symptoms or issues from his concussions. He HAS developed migraine headaches. He also has a family history of migraine on both sides of his family. Would he have developed migraines without his concussion history? I don't know. Did the concussions trigger the migraines that he may have already been pre-disposed to? Maybe. Nobody knows for sure. But, I do know he is the same quick-witted, funny and sweet kid that he's always been. He's excelling academically and he's able to participate in all of the activities that he loves. And for all of that, I am so very grateful!

My family feels lucky to have learned so much about this injury and this process of recovery. Our hope is that if Lucas's story reaches even one family, who in turn uses it to help a child navigate the very serious world of concussion recovery, and helps that child to achieve a better outcome due to approaching the injury differently than they otherwise would have, then we will be so very happy. There is nothing more precious than our babies, their health and their futures.

CHAPTER 7

A Conversation with the Specialists

I was fortunate enough to have the luxury and privilege of speaking to two of the most important members of Lucas's treatment team, his neurologist, Dr. John Dolan, D.O., of Southern Maine Medical Center and his physical therapist, Mike Hersey, PT, CSCS, of Southern Maine Health Care's Sports Performance Center. Both gentlemen have specialized training in youth concussion and were willing to spend some time with me answering questions.

Melissa: Thank you for taking the time to speak with me today. Let's jump right into this.

Why is it so important to rest your brain after a concussion?

Dr. Dolan: So, allowing your brain to rest after a concussion allows the normal physiology of the brain to return to its baseline. When you experience a concussion, you create a supply and demand mismatch, where the typical metabolic needs of the tissue, which is what goes on throughout your body at all times, where a particular system in your body, whether it's your digestive system or your musculoskeletal system, always gets the blood flow and the energy that it needs. During a concussion, you have a huge surge and a need for energy, due to the application of external force, whether it's a baseball bat or a soccer ball, or somebody's elbow hitting your head, you generate an exponentially larger demand, but no change in supply in regards to energy. So, you have a supply and demand mismatch. The only thing that you can control is the demand, so by resting your brain and avoiding things that require a high amount of energy consumption, you can lower the demand for energy, which makes it easier for that supply and demand mismatch to be resolved. Time and rest are required, with time being responsible for the supply side to come back on line and rest being responsible for the demand side to be limited. It narrows the gap and makes it easier for that to resolve itself.

Mike: So, you've got to allow everything to kind of calm down. It's very similar to an ankle sprain. If you have an ankle that's swollen you're not going to continue to go out and run on it, because the risk of re-injuring is that much more severe.

Melissa: How important is it to keep from exacerbating your symptoms after a concussion?

Dr. Dolan: The exacerbation of your symptoms is your body's way of telling you that you are exceeding the capabilities of the brain at that time. It's just like running when you have a sprained ankle. You run on it and you try and cut and your ankle hurts. When you have a concussion and you try and do 30 math problems, your symptoms get worse, and your symptoms get worse, whether it's headaches, dizziness or blurred vision, that's analogous to trying to cut on a sprained ankle.

Mike: So, it's all the same, especially with kids that don't understand this. They are going to try to push their limits. But, it's one of those things where the more you can control your symptoms, the better you are going to feel a little bit sooner. So, I think it's important for kids to just take a deep breath and relax and realize we want them to still do things but we don't want them to overdo it. It's an energy crisis within the brain, so we want them to be using their brain and not be on strict and utter bedrest, but at the same time continuing to use it, but not overdoing it. We're allowing the brain to be stimulated but not overworking and causing an increase in symptoms.

Melissa: Is there a danger in not properly healing after a concussion?

Dr. Dolan: Yes, there are a couple of different dangers. One, the longer you have symptoms or are stuck with the symptoms, predisposes you to post-concussion syndrome, which is this sustained gap that would require medications and other interventions. Two, if you try and return to play before you have resolution of your symptoms, then you are exposing yourself to the risk of secondary impact syndrome. Secondary impact syndrome is a phenomenon where you re-injure the brain before it's fully healed and the application of lesser force produces bigger pathologic changes that can range from more pronounced symptoms all the way to catastrophic swelling and death. And there's no way to tell what's going to happen, so you have to go through, what's referred to as a return to play protocol.

Mike: There was a great rat study done over in Europe a few years back that kind of highlights it. They dropped a 10 lb. weight on a rat's head. The rat was fine within a week or two. They dropped a 5 lb. weight on a different rat's head, and 5 minutes later dropped a second 5 lb. weight on that same rat's head and that rat died. So, that's why it's very important to rest after a concussion.

Melissa: What are the potential long-term effects of not healing properly from a concussion?

Dr. Dolan: The jury is probably still out on that. We don't know exactly what the "n" or number is of concussions that you have to be exposed to, to be at risk for severe long-term sequelae, whether it's subtle changes in how you learn, some subtle changes with memory, subtle changes in behavior, long term problems with eye movement, problems with balance, all the way out to CTE, which is chronic traumatic encephalopathy, which is what gets all of the press. We don't know what that specific number is, nor do we know if that certain number is predictable. That means that individual A and individual B get the same number of concussions. Only one of them may go on to develop CTE and one doesn't, and we don't really have a great grasp of what that looks like or why.

Melissa: So, there's no magic number of concussions to put a hard stop on risky activities?

Dr. Dolan: Right. There's no magic number. In terms of short-term impact, there are different guidelines out there. A good rule of thumb is if you sustain three documented concussions inside of a particular calendar year in the younger population, or in student athletes, then that is a hard stop for at least 6 months for dedicated brain rest and should probably be a year of being out of risk behaviors or activities.

Melissa: What are the potential long-term effects of sustaining multiple concussions?

Dr. Dolan: CTE is the big one. Changes in learning, changes in attention, changes in concentration, mood changes, headaches. Headaches is probably the most common. It's the development of a concussion related headache syndrome. Sometimes it's just tension type headaches. Sometimes it can be the development of migraines, from episodic all the way to chronic for both.

Melissa: We talked about this in the short-term, but once a child has experienced a concussion, is he/she more prone to develop subsequent concussions at a later time frame in the future?

Dr. Dolan: Yes. The hardest concussion to get is your first one. Once you've had your first concussion, it's easier to get a second. Then, it's easier to get a third and so on, down the road. We can't quantify what that risk is. So, it's not as if I can say, "Okay, you've had one concussion. You're twice as likely to get your second." It probably isn't a doubling of risk, but it does mean that you are at a slightly higher risk than the general population. It's just like any other old injury. It's easier to aggravate it moving forward.

Melissa: Mike, I know you and the physicians work as a team. Tell me about how that works. When and why is it important to have a physical therapist on board after a concussion?

Mike: It's an even bigger picture than that. I think the more that we have licensed athletic trainers on the sidelines that can spot the symptoms, the better. Unfortunately, kids playing youth sports, I see it quite often where a kid is looking dazed and confused and the coach immediately puts them right back into the game or into the next play. I think it's important for somebody to be there as a spotter. Athletic trainers do a very good job of spotting and trying to grab a kid and keep that kid out. It's better to be safe than sorry with a concussion. I'd rather misdiagnose a concussion during a game or a practice than to be wrong and potentially have something more severe happen.

As far as rehab is concerned, it's those ones that linger, that initially they are dizzy or extremely foggy or their convergence is way off. We know that those are going to linger out about a month. It's then getting that physician on board immediately, so that A) we can start to monitor things and have a baseline and B) in case medication needs to be part of it down the line, they can start that medical intervention. Also, the dizziness, fogginess, convergence insufficiency…by bringing physical therapy on board more quickly, and starting those exercises, especially for oculomotor activities, and also trying to ease any anxiety that may be around the concussion as well initially. So, getting more people involved initially can kind of calm, especially a kid, who may already have some anxiety. Getting them into physical therapy sooner, can kind of ease them and let them know, "Hey, these do get better. Eventually, you are going to feel good."

Melissa: You mentioned convergence. Can you please explain what that is?

Mike: Yes. The goal of convergence is our eyes should be able to converge on an object coming towards them, typically, right around that 4-7cm spot. We know that all of a sudden, if a kid is seeing double at 14 cm or greater, then their risk of having lingering symptoms is that much more likely. It's actually 8 times more likely, per the newest study, that they're going to take more than a month to get better. It's just the ability for the eyes to focus.

Melissa: I've learned that oculomotor spasms are quite common with concussions. What is the relationship between oculomotor spasm and concussion?

Mike: There are actually 6 different types of concussions that we like to categorize, one of them being oculomotor. It's that everything should fire correctly within the brain, and we know that energy crisis is going on within the brain. So, the eyes obviously work together with either side of the brain. So, when one side of the brain is maybe a little bit slower than the other side, there's that little synapse issue within the brain. You're going to see that with those oculomotor activities. Probably the best way to put it is, it's that energy crisis being seen by somebody else, where you can see that eye start to jump. You can see nystagmus in one eye. Typically, it's going to be unilateral. I have seen a couple of bilaterals, but usually it's going to be one side, and it's usually going to be the side where the impact to the head took place.

Melissa: You mentioned 6 types of concussions. What are the other 5 types?

Mike: There is cervico-genic, which is more of that whiplash type patient, where they kind of get cervico-muscular spasms. Those cause more tension headaches. You have vestibular, where you've got the crystals within the ears. You get some crystallization within the tubes within the ears. You're going to start to get vertigo, for lack of a better term. You're going to start to feel dizzy all the time. Those ones we love because those ones we can make feel better really, really quick. You have emotional components to concussions as well. Lastly, there's just the mechanical blow to the head. If I hit my head against the wall right now, my head is going to ache in that spot, and it may linger for a day or two, depending on the severity. Typically, those ones resolve pretty quickly. The ones that tend to linger are the oculomotor and the emotional ones. If you have an emotional one with oculomotor, sometimes that can really take a while to get better. The big thing with emotional concussions is that kids who are more fearful of having concussions, their symptoms are going to linger longer than a kid who doesn't even know what a concussion is. So, we can definitely tell when there is that emotional component, which is why we are now trying to get kids out and about, put kids back in school earlier, let kids be around their friends more often, allow kids to exercise. Ten or 15 years ago, we didn't let kids do these things at all, and we were finding that we were actually doing more harm than good and probably inducing some of that emotional component, rather than letting them hang out a little with their friends, let them watch some tv, let them play on their computer. You can't take away a kid's entire social life or else you're going to start to induce some of that emotional component.

Melissa: Obviously, concussion rehab has come a long way since the days of "just go home and rest". You mentioned the different types of concussions, so I'm assuming those are some of the things you evaluate and look for during an initial physical therapy evaluation. What other things do you look for and what does concussion rehab look like?

Mike: So, one of the things that we look for initially is a way to classify into one of the ladders, like which way am I going to go with this. A lot of times there will be two portions of the six involved. That can happen frequently, especially depending on how long it takes until they get here. We just saw a girl a month ago who had headaches when she was 15. She had a concussion when she was 15, a second concussion at 16, and then just had another concussion at 22. Once we dug down into it, we realized that she had never improved from the one she had in high school. She always had academic accommodations and always struggled academically. The first day we saw her I told her she needed prism lenses. I told her I didn't know if this was something long-term or something from her most recent concussion, but that she definitely needed prism lenses because her convergence was way off the charts. She went to visual rehabilitation and she's doing a lot better. Come to find out, the concussion she came here for was one of those ones that was just going to get better really quickly, however, the one that she had back in high school had never gotten better. So, it's spotting things like that and figuring out which way we're going to go.

A lot of times the first day is more educational. If it's vestibular, we'll treat them right away, that day. The vestibular rehab technique can definitely make those feel a lot better pretty quickly. For visual concussions, we're going to do a lot of visual exercises. For the cervico-genic ones, which can be a little bit trickier, we're going to do a lot of hands on manual therapy, mobilizations to the thoracic spine and cervical spine, myofascial release techniques to try and relax some of those spasms that people have been having. Also, on the first day, we try to figure out what are the long term goals going to be for myself and for the patient.

The first day we do spend time evaluating the family as well. I have had a mother in the past, where I had to ask her to stop asking her daughter how often her daughter was having headaches. We looked at her daughter's phone. She would send a text message about every half hour asking her how her headaches were doing. If I sit here, in this room right now, and tell myself, "I have a headache. I have a headache," over and over again, after a while I'm going to give myself a headache. The mom, initially, was none too impressed with me, but later on figured out what I was saying and why. I told her she was allowed to ask her daughter, once a day, how she was feeling. Other than that, I told her she was allowed to have a relationship with her daughter. I told her that her daughter was not broken, she was going to get better, and we have to all work together to allow her to get better. So, it's evaluating some of those family dynamics sometimes, too. Last, but not least, we look for secondary gains. I feel like we've seen more of this over the past couple of years. There are some kids who don't want to play sports. There are some kids who just want to be on the team. Sometimes, there are kids who think they should be getting more playing time, but don't want to work to get the playing time, and they will come up with symptoms. Unfortunately, we're seeing more of that. We treat that more like the emotional concussion, where we don't really find anything on the examination, but when you do the neurocognitive test, you can kind of see that they're sandbagging the test a little bit. We use the ImPACT test here in this clinic. Once again, if there's something emotional going on there, we do try to treat that like a concussion. Usually, with those, by the time their season winds down, they're starting to feel better. We don't usually put a lot of academic restrictions on those kids, but we put a ton of athletic restrictions on those kids. It's sometimes a little trickier, but also for peer support, you don't want to completely call that kid out and say, "Hey, you're faking this."

Melissa: Wow. There's definitely a lot to this. That was a really interesting story about the young lady with the headaches. Do you think that if she had been seen after her concussion when she was 15, and it would have been resolved, do you think it would have prevented where she is at now?

Mike: I think convergence insufficiency, at that point, was just becoming a hot word. She did go through therapy back then, and with the tools they had back then, they did tell her she was probably as good as she was going to get. She also had occupational therapy to determine academic accommodations. At that point, she even tried doing speech therapy to no avail. It's one of those things that has become more of a hot topic in the last 5-6 years.

Melissa: So, let's say that whole pattern started today. Do you think the outcome would be different or some of her problems would be resolved earlier in the process?

Mike: Yes. I had another kid last volleyball season, who had been seen for two concussions prior, and she said she kept getting headaches but they were migraines. I saw her after a volleyball injury and told her I wasn't so sure they were and sent her off to neuro-opthalmology. She got so much better from having the prism glasses and she told me she doesn't have migraines anymore.

Melissa: So, the prism lenses that you are referring to, are those something that are worn permanently until the end of time or just until the symptoms are resolved?

Mike: The neuro-opthalmologists that we work with all say you're at least in them for a year and a half, but people usually start seeing the difference almost immediately.

Melissa: If proper rest and rehabilitation take place after a concussion, does that change the risk of sustaining future concussions?

Dr. Dolan: It doesn't change the risk, but it allows us to return that student athlete back to play in as safe a manner as we possibly can. We all want to wrap our kids in bubble wrap and keep them from ever sustaining any kind of injury, but that's just not realistic. If we go through the proper rest so that they are asymptomatic, the proper rehabilitation with the graduated exercise program, and depending on what's required as far as physical therapy or occupational therapy, if necessary, then repeat cognitive testing, showing a return to baseline, then data suggests that that's as close to perfect as we are going to come. That's getting you back to where you were pre-injury. We accept that there's going to be a slight increased risk in the future. We can't quantify it. We know it's small, but it ultimately becomes a decision to be made between parent and child as far as whether continuing certain activities, is a good idea.

Melissa: If proper rest and rehabilitation take place, does it change the risk of long-term damage?

Dr. Dolan: With proper rest and rehabilitation and return to baseline, and you have documented proof of that, kind of shows there hasn't been any long-term sequelae. So, as long as you can continue to do that, you can continue to be cleared. Once you can't do that, then there's a problem. You don't get to return to play and that indicates that there may need to be a change in your risk activity.

Melissa: For a child that has experienced

a concussion, do you recommend follow up testing or imaging, later on down the road?

Dr. Dolan: No. As long as they come back to baseline, there's really no indication that they will require any advanced neuro-imaging, CT scans or MRIs. A vast majority of the time, those tests are not helpful in the diagnosis of a concussion. The biggest piece that is done at this time is baseline cognitive testing. The ImPACT test is the most common one used here and that is almost ubiquitous at the high school level and it's beginning to trickle down into middle school. Once that test has been performed, it should be repeated every 2 years or after an injury to the head.

Melissa: What information does that testing give you?

Dr. Dolan: It establishes some baseline performance metrics with regards to verbal memory, visual memory, visual processing speed and reaction time. It's very easy to target, easy to capture data points on how the brain is functionally doing. We know that athletes want to be athletes, which means players want to play, and sometimes they will try to sandbag us and say their symptoms are fine. In saying that, we believe them and if their exam is normal, in the absence of the baseline impact testing, we may put them at undue risk. So, having this information allows us to say, "Yes, you may be feeling better and you're back to normal exam wise, but your reaction time is still too slow. You haven't gone back to baseline and that indicates that your brain isn't fully healed." It's an added layer of protection for the athlete.

Melissa: Mike, how do you incorporate baseline testing into therapy? Is that something that is automatically performed across the board when somebody comes in with a concussion? How does that work?

Mike: Yeah, it's great if we actually have a baseline when somebody comes in. If we have that, then we can do a post-injury day 1 test and that makes our lives a lot easier. There are some studies out there, from Pittsburgh, showing potential length of time for recovery, based on how they perform on that ImPACT test. So, essentially it gives us one more tool. It's not the end all, be all, but it is good to see neuro-cognitively where the kid is at the day after and then where they're at once they've gone through their return to play progression.

Melissa: Other than when somebody first experiences a concussion, when else would you recommend having the initial testing done?

Dr. Dolan: Currently, at least locally, any high school that is a part of the Maine Concussion Management Coalition, tests any students who are involved in risk sports beginning their freshman year.

Melissa: Which sports are considered risk sports?

Dr. Dolan: Right now they are doing soccer, field hockey, lacrosse, football, basketball and hockey.

Melissa: Mike, do you recommend being seen in therapy each time you have a concussion or can someone use what they've learned in therapy previously at home?

Mike: I think it's good to have someone medically watching over you no matter what, before you go back to play. You're not going to know if you have nystagmus. You're not going to know if your balance is off a little bit. You're not going to know what your convergence is. And I think that parents are starting to recognize, too, that it's better to be safe than sorry. Someone should definitely be watching over you medically, whether it's a primary care physician, a PT, an athletic trainer, a neurologist, but somebody should be helping out with that. It shouldn't just be a parent because sometimes a parent can be a little jaded.

Melissa: Recognition and discussion of CTE is relatively new. For some of those grown athletes with CTE, if they had been followed the way that young athletes are followed now, do you think we would still see the same number of cases of CTE? Would someone have seen that ahead of time, before they got to that point?

Dr. Dolan: The answer is probably yes. There has certainly been a dramatic shift in the way we look at concussions and how we treat concussions and how we intervene on concussions at the earlier ages. How that's going to impact things long-term, we're not going to know for a decade or more. Could some of these athletes have been diverted away from their sports earlier? Probably so. The idea is if we can identify the individuals at risk, the individuals who are not recovering the way that we would expect them to, with a dedicated and structured protocol, then we can start to early identify those who are showing a risk pattern. When you can't recover and you start to get into post-concussion syndrome, persistent headaches, persistent trouble with concentration, behavioral changes, visual changes, that extend outside of 90 days from the original concussion injury, and that change the way you perform on a day to day basis, those are the folks we want to be able to identify and divert away from those risky activities. I think the jury is out on whether we would have been able to prevent some of the headlines associated with CTE.

Melissa: When does a concussion become post-concussion syndrome?

Dr. Dolan: It's based on the presence of a concussion, the persistent presence of symptoms, 90 days from the original event, and a functional impact. So, if you have a concussion, and you are completely back to baseline with the exception of occasional headaches, that occur randomly and are not tethered to physical activity or cognitive activity, that's not post-concussion syndrome. If you have a concussion, you're 3 months out, and you're still out of work or school because bright lights bother you or you're off balance, you have blurred vision, that's post-concussion syndrome.

Melissa: We talked about the fact that there is no magic number, but at what point do you suggest that a child refrain from certain activities or risk activities?

Dr. Dolan: Absolute hard-stop 3 concussions in a calendar year, with 6-12 months of brain rest, meaning no risk activities. After that, it really is a decision that's made based on the athlete's recovery profile. At that point, it becomes a discussion with that child's parents and the child that the physician would have to have. You have to determine what risk you want your kid to be exposed to. That's going to be variable as well.

Mike: I've never held a kid out of a sport based on number of concussions. That's more of a parent/athlete conversation. That's a tricky question. I think if the determination is to allow a kid to participate in a risky sport, you just have to try to make them as safe as possible. I can't say I'd ever tell a kid not to participate in a sport. There are CTE studies coming out now where non-athletes are having CTE as well.

Melissa: What if a child falls behind in school while recovering from a concussion? Are there laws or rules in place to protect students so they can feel confident in following their treatment plan, even if it includes missing or restricting school?

Mike: This, again, is something that has been a hot topic in the last 10 years. Initially, we do put them on academic restrictions. Almost everyone is placed on academic restrictions immediately afterwards and then we start to loosen them over the next 1-2 weeks. It's only about 1-2 times a year that we actually have to get guidance involved and start a kid down a 504 plan. That's a legal document stating accommodations that a kid has to have in the school. They are covered by the Americans with Disabilities Act when they are concussed. It is a gray area though. We hope that teachers are willing to work with kids to help them determine what is absolutely essential work to be completed, versus non-essential work.

Melissa: You mentioned headaches and migraines, but can someone develop other medical conditions due to having a history of concussions?

Dr. Dolan: They are trying to link a number of concussions, the "n" being a moving target, to developing long-term memory problems. They are trying to link it to things like dementia. They are trying to link concussions to other neurodegenerative disorders like motor neuron disease or ALS (Lou Gehrig's disease). That has been less successful. There is certainly no cause/effect relationship, even though it is discussed as a potential cause/effect relationship. The path from A to B is convoluted at best. In general, the big things that we look for are memory, attention, focus, and concentration.

Melissa: So, other than avoiding risk activities, which is still not a given, are there any ways to prevent concussions?

Dr. Dolan: Avoiding risk activities is huge and making sure you engage in proper training year round before you engage in those risk activities.

Melissa: So, do you mean strength training?

Dr. Dolan: Yep, strength training. There is a disparity in terms of sports concussion rates. In particular, there is a higher concussion rate per hour played in girls' soccer vs boys' soccer. They try to link that back to core strength, neck strength, so it is advised to engage in proper fitness for what you are going to do. That's really the best way. When you are engaged in certain risk activities, proper fitting helmets are key. The helmets should have a shelf life. You don't want to give the helmet that you used in youth football to your kid. The technology is ever evolving, so the latest and greatest is always important. There are some commercially available concussion specific head gear for sports like soccer, field hockey and basketball, where you are allowed to have some type of device in place. There's no data to say they reduce the rate of concussions, but the basic science on how they work is good. It's basically energy dispersion. So, the design of these devices tries to disperse the energy as opposed to allow for a much more forceful, direct energy that seems to be associated with a higher risk of concussion. But, there's no data that that works.

Mike: At one of the local high schools right now, they are using sensors in the football helmets. The sensors aren't going to tell us anything except for, wow, that was a big enough hit, we should probably take a look at that kid. The other thing it can tell us is if we see 15 kids spiking at the same time every day or week, we should probably take a look at the drill that's being done at that time. If we see one kid that is always spiking at the same time every week, we should look at the way that kid is tackling. I think that is going to help both coaches and athletic trainers a little more. But, as far as preventing concussions, other than putting a kid in a bubble, there's really no way to prevent them.

Melissa: What is the #1 thing that you would want parents to know should their child sustain a concussion?

Dr. Dolan: Do everything you can to control the environment for your child. By that I mean, encourage the concept of structured rest and reactive rest. Your child has sustained a concussion, so you need to clamp down on having a routine; a set bedtime, a set wake time. You ensure that they are eating and drinking appropriately. They need to avoid triggers, cutting back on screen time, cutting back on cell phones and laptops and iPads and gaming systems. They need lots of fluids, clear liquids, juices and making sure to stay really well hydrated. Avoid things like caffeine, energy drinks. Cut sports drinks in half, for instance, half Gatorade, half water, to avoid sugar. The sugar actually dehydrates you. Caffeine is obviously a stimulant, so that can increase the energy demand of the brain. For reactive rest, you encourage your child to be honest about their symptoms because if they're not, they're going to have their symptoms more. The more and longer you have those symptoms, the longer you're stuck with the symptoms, which means a longer recovery phase. So, it's important to get the child on board with recognizing the importance of structured rest in the same way you would rest a sprained ankle or rest a broken arm. You don't have a choice but to rest those body parts if you're wearing a brace or a cast, but your brain requires that rest as well. An increase in your concussion symptoms is analogous to the symptom of your ankle throbbing if you run on it after you sprain it. So, that rest in the setting of symptoms is really, really important. And know that no two concussions are alike. Child A and child B can have the exact same injury. Child A may be better 5 days, 7 days or 10 days earlier than child B. There is no rhyme or reason for that. It is what it is. You accept it for what it is. You have to put that child in the right position to get better as quickly as they can, knowing that 95+% of the time, kids are going to get better regardless of what we do as parents or physicians, within the first 1-3 or 2-4 weeks. That's the natural history of this. We just want to set them up for success the best we can. There's not even a reliable, predictable outcome when a single athlete has multiple concussions. The first event may be a lot quicker to recover from than their second. Their second might be a lot longer to recover from than their third. We just don't know.

Mike: Seek medical advice and play it smart. When in doubt, keep them out.

Melissa: This is all so great and helpful for me as a parent of a very active child. Thank you so much for sharing your time and expertise with me. I just know there are a lot of families that will definitely be helped by having this information.

GLOSSARY OF TERMS

Americans with Disabilities Act - The Americans with Disabilities Act (ADA) is federal legislation passed in 1990 that prohibits discrimination against people with disabilities. ... The law prohibits private employers, state and local governments, employment agencies, and labor unions from discriminating against the disabled. (www.investopedia.com)

athletic trainer - an athletic trainer is a certified and licensed health care professional who practices in the field of sports medicine. Athletic training has been recognized by the American Medical Association (AMA) as an allied health care profession since 1990. (www.wikipedia. org)

chiropractic neurologist - a chiropractic neurologist is a chiropractor who specializes in working with patients who have neurological issues.

concussion – a concussion is a type of traumatic brain injury—or TBI—caused by a bump, blow, or jolt to the head or by a hit to the body that causes the head and brain to move rapidly back and forth. (www.cdc.org)

concussion specialist - a concussion specialist is a licensed health care professional certified in identifying, treating, and managing mild traumatic brain injury (mTBI) in patients. (www.sports-health.com)

convergence - coordinated movement of the two eyes so that the image of a single point is formed on corresponding retinal areas. (www.merriam-webster.com)

CTE (chronic traumatic encephalopathy) - a progressive degenerative disease of the brain found in people with a history of repetitive brain trauma (often athletes), including symptomatic concussions as well as asymptomatic sub-concussive hits to the head that do not cause symptoms. (www.bu.edu)

ImPACT test - an FDA cleared online tool for baseline and post-injury testing, measures visual and verbal memory, reaction time, and processing speed to help determine if a patient (ages 12-59) can safely return to activity. (<u>www.</u><u>impactconcussion.com</u>)

migraine - a powerful headache that often happens with nausea, vomiting, and sensitivity to light. (<u>www.webmd.com</u>)

MRI (magnetic resonance imaging) - a medical imaging technique that uses a magnetic field and computer-generated radio waves to create detailed images of the organs and tissues in your body. (<u>www.mayoclinic.org</u>)

Neuro-behavioral optometry – an extended study of optometry that treats the visual impairment of the eyes due to brain trauma. (<u>www.bfeye.com</u>)

neurologist – a medical doctor concerned with the study and treatment of disorders of the nervous system

nystagmus - rapid involuntary movements of the eyes. (Oxford dictionary)

occupational therapist – a licensed practitioner offering therapy for those recuperating from physical or mental illness that encourages rehabilitation through the performance of activities required in daily life. (Oxford dictionary)

oculomotor - relating to the motion of the eye. (Oxford dictionary)

physical therapist - Physical therapists (PTs) are movement experts who optimize quality of life through prescribed exercise, hands-on care, and patient education. (www.apta.org)

post-concussion syndrome - a complex disorder in which various symptoms — such as headaches and dizziness that last for weeks and sometimes months after the injury that caused the concussion. (www.mayoclinic.org)

prism lenses – eye glasses used to help correct double vision

secondary impact syndrome - occurs when the brain swells rapidly, and catastrophically, after a person suffers a second concussion before symptoms from an earlier one have subsided. This second blow may occur minutes, days or weeks after an initial concussion, and even the mildest grade of concussion can lead to SIS. (en. wikipedia.org)

REFERENCES

1. "Concussion" American Association of Neurological Surgeons. (2019) Retrieved from www.aans.org

2. "Concussion: Symptoms, Causes, Diagnosis, Treatments & Recovery" WebMD. (September 16, 2018) Retrieved from www.webmd.com

3. Perrine, Ph.D., Kenneth. (November 2014) "Diagnosing and Treating Concussion" Weill Cornell Brain and Spine Center. Retrieved from www.concussion.weillcornell.org

4. Munday, Ph.D., Claude, Lynch, Ph.D., William, Haller, John, Traumatic Brain and Spinal Cord Injury Project, San Jose, CA. (1996) "Coping with Behavioral Problems after Head Injury" Family Caregiver Alliance. Retrieved from www.caregiver.org

Made in the USA
Middletown, DE
31 December 2019